Hello Friends!

Places I Know

Imagine That!

Oh, What Fun!

Let's Go Outside

What a Funny Animal!

IMAGINATION
An Odyssey Through Language

Let's Go
Outside

Gail Heald-Taylor
General Consultant, Language Arts

HBJ **HARCOURT BRACE JOVANOVICH, PUBLISHERS**

Orlando   San Diego   Chicago   Dallas

Acknowledgments

For permission to reprint copyrighted material, grateful acknowledgment is made to the following sources:

Harcourt Brace Jovanovich Inc.: I Love You, Mouse by John Graham, pictures by Tomie dePaola. Text copyright © 1976 by John Graham; illustrations copyright © 1976 by Tomie dePaola.

Harper & Row, Publishers, Inc.: Abridged text and illustrations from *What Is Beyond the Hill?*, written by Ernst A. Ekker, illustrated by Hilde Heyduck-Huth. Text copyright © 1985 by Ernst A. Ekker; translation copyright © 1986 by Harper & Row, Publishers, Inc.; illustrations copyright © 1985 by Hilde Heyduck-Huth. Published by J. B. Lippincott.

Gina Maccoby Literary Agency: "Hello and Good-by" (Retitled: "Hello and Good-bye") from *Hello and Good-by* by Mary Ann Hoberman. Copyright © 1959, renewed 1987 by Mary Ann Hoberman. Published by Little, Brown and Company.

William Morrow & Company, Inc.: Coco Can't Wait! (Hayaku Aitaina) by Taro Gomi. Copyright © 1979 by Taro Gomi; English translation copyright © 1983 by William Morrow and Company, Inc.

Philomel Books: Beside the Bay by Sheila White Samton. Text and illustrations copyright © 1987 by Sheila White Samton.

Art Credits

Cheryl Arnemann: 81-83; Taro Gomi: 2-31; Hilde Heyduck-Huth: 58-75; Tomie dePaola: 32-57; Cathy Pavia: 76-80; Peter Spier: 84-93

Cover: Tom Vroman

Contents

Hello Friends!

Places I Know

Imagine That!

Oh, What Fun!

Let's Go Outside

What a Funny Animal!

Coco Can't Wait!

A story by Taro Gomi

Coco lives on top of the hill, in the house with the purple roof.

Grandma lives on the mountain, in
the house with the orange roof.

One day Coco wanted to see
Grandma very much.

And Grandma wanted to see Coco
very much.

"Dear me! Coco is not here!"

"Oh no! Grandma is not here!"

"Oh no! Grandma is not here!"

"Dear me! Coco is not here!"

"I can't wait any longer."

"There isn't a minute to lose."

"Oh, how I want to see Grandma."

"Oh, how I want to see Coco."

"Hello, Grandma!"

"Hello, Coco!"

"Next time, Grandma, let's meet in
the middle, right under this tree."
And Grandma and Coco ate all the
apples in Grandma's basket.

I Love You, Mouse

From a story by John Graham

Pictures by Tomie dePaola

I love you, mouse,

and if I were a mouse,
I'd make you a furry nest.
And we'd curl up together
and nibble some cheese.

I love you, kitten,

34

and if I were a cat,
I'd make you a soft basket.
And we'd drink warm milk
and stretch ourselves.

I love you, puppy,

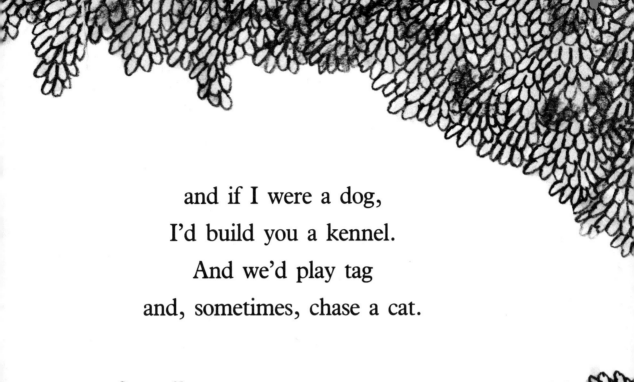

and if I were a dog,
I'd build you a kennel.
And we'd play tag
and, sometimes, chase a cat.

I love you, piglet,

and if I were a pig,
I'd build you a sty.
And we'd dig roots
and loaf in the mud.

I love you, chicky,

and if I were a chicken,
I'd build you a coop.
And we'd scratch for corn
and chase a butterfly.

I love you, lamb,

and if I were a sheep,
I'd build you a strong fold.
And we'd graze in the pasture
and grow wool for sweaters.

I love you, cub,

and if I were a bear,
I'd find you a cozy cave.
And we'd hunt for some honey
and watch out for bees.

I love you, tadpole,

and if I were a frog,
I'd find a quiet pond.
And we'd splash in the pond
and have races you'd win.

I love you, duckling,

and if I were a duck,
I'd find a blue lake.
And we'd swim all day long
and go "quack-quack."

I love you, gosling,

and if I were a goose,
I'd find a wide marsh.
And we'd play hide-and-seek among cattails
and go "honk-honk."

I love you, bunny,

and if I were a rabbit,
I'd find you a safe burrow.
And we'd play in the moonlight
and eat clover and carrots.

I love you, owlet,

and if I were an owl,
I'd find you a warm tree hole.
And we'd fly together, all night long,
and call out "who-who."

I love you, baby,

and since we're people,
I've built a house for you,
and given you a bed with warm quilts,
a cool drink of water,
a kiss on the nose,
and a quiet good-night.

What Is Beyond the Hill?

A story by Ernst A. Ekker

What is beyond the hill?

Does the world stop there?

No, the world does not stop there.

Beyond the hill, there is another hill.

Beyond that hill is another hill and
another hill and still another hill.

But the world does not stop there.

Then there is a mountain.

And what is beyond the mountain?
Does the world stop there?

Beyond that mountain is another
mountain

and another mountain and another
mountain and another mountain.

But the world does not stop there.
Beyond the mountains is a star.

The world does not stop there.

And what is beyond the star?

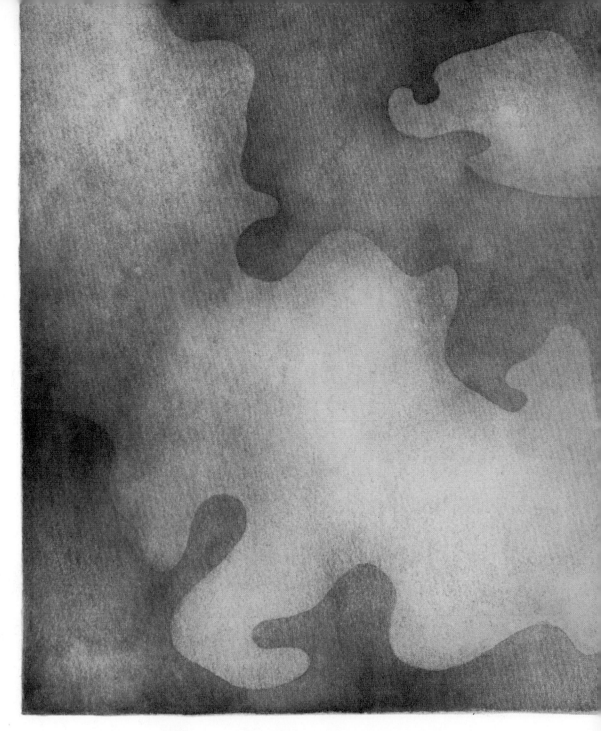

The world does not stop there.

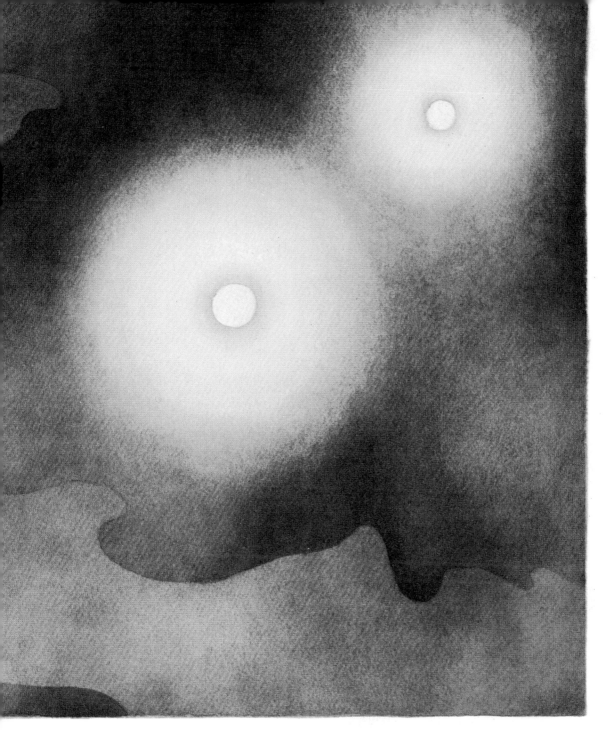

Beyond the star is another star.

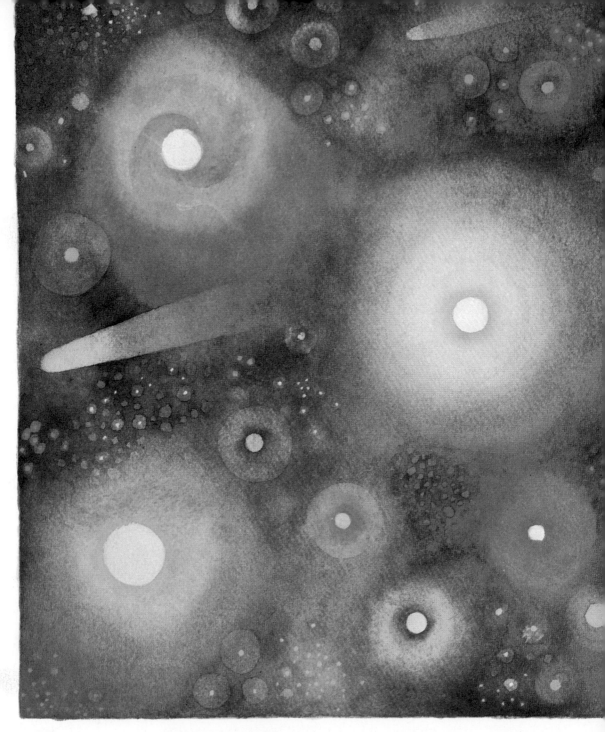

Beyond that star is another star and
another star and another star . . .

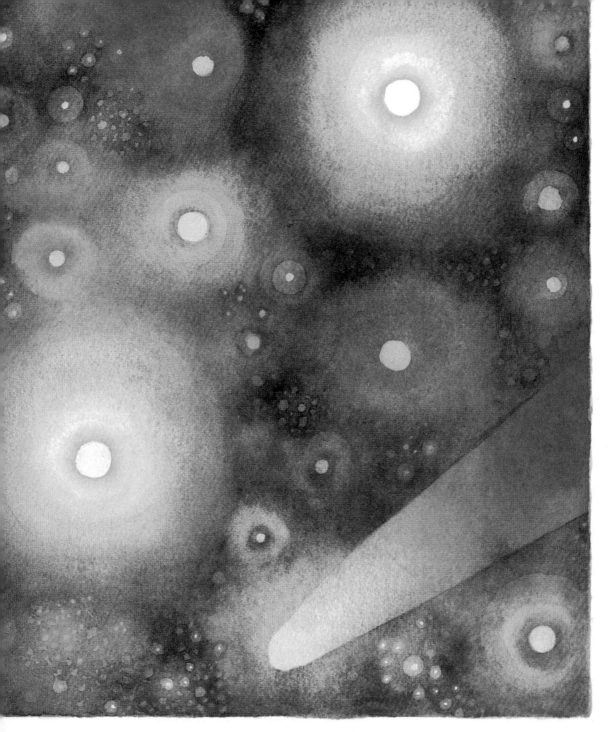

and another star and still another star.
And the stars go on forever.

Connections

Water

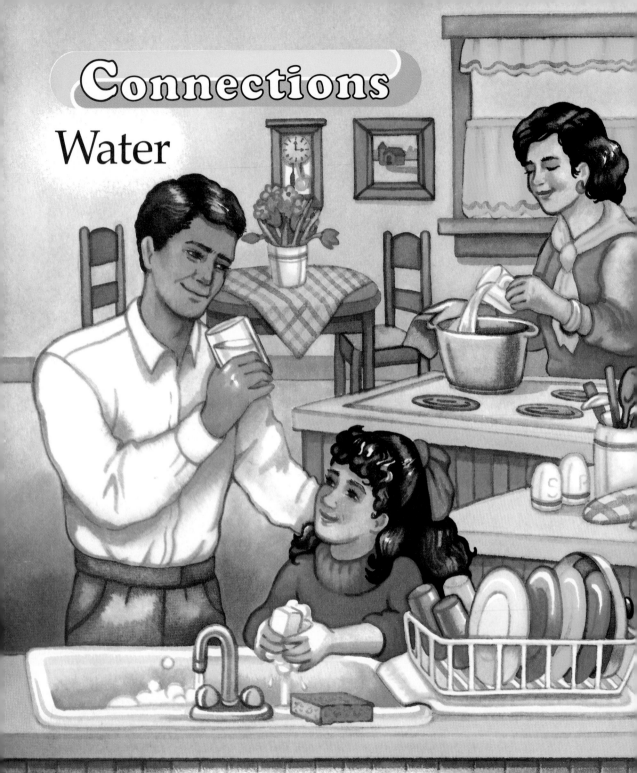

We use water at home.

Water is cool on a hot day.

Boats help us travel on water.

Some animals live in water.

We need water to grow food.

Hello and Good-bye

A poem by Mary Ann Hoberman

Hello and good-bye
Hello and good-bye

When I'm in a swing
Swinging low and then high
Good-bye to the ground
Hello to the sky.

Pictures by Cheryl Arnemann

Hello to the rain
Good-bye to the sun,
Then hello again sun
When the rain is all done.

In blows the winter,
Away the birds fly.
Good-bye and hello
Hello and good-bye.

Beside the Bay

A story by Sheila White Samton

I walk alone beside the bay,

The water's blue, the sky is gray.

There is no sun or shade at all,

Just white clouds and a white stone wall.

A yellow lizard family

Walks right along the wall with me.

A pink snail in a pink seashell

Walks along with me as well.

And from behind I hear the purr

Of an orange cat, with orange fur.

93

The stones are set in rows and stacks,

And blackbirds nest between the cracks

Until they fly off on the breeze,

Out to an island of green trees.

Out in the bay the island floats,

Behind the red sails of the boats.

And flying fish, with purple scales,

Flick drops of water from their tails.

How deeply gray the sky has grown!

And we are on this wall alone.

But now I hear my brown dog's bark.

He's come to bring me home by dark.

My walk beside the bay is through.

The sky's still gray, the water blue.